HiIiJjKkLlMmNnOoPp
YyZzAaBbCcDdEeF
OoPpQqRrSsTtUuV
EeFfGgHhIiJjKkLl
uUvVwWXxYyZzAaB
KlLlMmNnOoPpQqR
AaBbCcDdEeF

FEB -- 2006

PL

D1401351

ALPHABAD

ALPHABAD

Shannon Stewart Illustrated by Dušan Petričić

KPk
Key Porter Kids

Copyright text © 2005 Shannon Stewart
Copyright illustrations © 2005 Dušan Petričić

All rights reserved. No part of this work covered by the copyrights hereon may be reproduced or used in any form or by any means—graphic, electronic or mechanical, including photocopying, recording, taping or information storage and retrieval systems—without the prior written permission of the publisher, or, in case of photocopying or other reprographic copying, a licence from Access Copyright, the Canadian Copyright Licensing Agency, One Yonge Street, Suite 1900, Toronto, Ontario, M6B 3A9.

Library and Archives Canada Cataloguing in Publication

Stewart, Shannon, 1966-
  Alphabad / Shannon Stewart ; Illustrated by Dušan Petričić.

ISBN 1-55263-729-8

1. English language—Alphabet—Juvenile literature. I. Petričić, Dušan II. Title.

PE1155.S744 2005   j421'.1   C2005-902704-5

The publisher gratefully acknowledges the support of the Canada Council for the Arts and the Ontario Arts Council for its publishing program. We acknowledge the support of the Government of Ontario through the Ontario Media Development Corporation's Ontario Book Initiative.

We acknowledge the financial support of the Government of Canada through the Book Publishing Industry Development Program (BPIDP) for our publishing activities.

KPk is an imprint of
Key Porter Books Limited
Six Adelaide Street East
Tenth Floor
Toronto, Ontario
Canada M5C 1H6

www.keyporter.com

Design: Peter Maher

Printed and bound in China
05 06 07 08 09 6 5 4 3 2 1

For my abcedarians, Gabrielle and Jacob—SS

For Andrej, my always amazed grandson—DP

A is for

atrocious.
An astronaut
attacking
aliens with
avocados is
atrocious.

B is for boobytrap.
Beastly brats set boobytraps for their babysitters.

C is for camouflage. Clever camouflage will not get you any closer to those coconut cookies.

D

is for dangerous.
Dressing Dad in a diaper
could be dangerous.

E is for excuse.

pushing extra buttons on the elevator requires an excellent excuse.

F is for **filthy.**
Filthy feet off the fancy furniture!

G

is for
grim.
A ghastly
gang of
groaning
ghouls
is very
grim.

H is for horrible.

Hiding behind hedges is a horrible habit.

I is for impolite.

Interrupting important conversations is impolite.

J is for jitters. Practising judo on a long journey gives drivers the jitters.

K is for Kooky.
A kingdom of kooky kids
is called a kindergarten.

L is for lies

Telling lies leads to lengthy lectures.

M

M is for mischief. Mischief in malls makes mommy mad.

N is for naughty.

Running naked through the neighbourhood is very naughty.

O is for ogre. offices are not obstacle courses for orienteering ogres.

P

is for pickle.

Pickles are not peculiar rockets from another planet. Please put them on your plate!

Q is for quarrel.
A quartet of quarrelling kids should be quarantined.

R

is for rude. Roaring in restaurants is rude.

**S** is for spying.

Spying on sister's special secrets is a sly and splendid sport.

T is for trouble.
A troop of
toddlers on
tricycles
is trouble.

U is for

unruly.

Unruly urchins
put umbrellas to
unpredictable
uses.

V is for viking.
Little vikings should avoid valuable vases.

W is for wicked.

writing words
on the wall
is wicked.

X

is for
extra bad.
Exploding xylophone
experiments can
be extra bad.

Y

is for yell.
youngsters who
yell in the yard
should live
in a yurt.

Z

Z is for zany.

zany alphabad kids
belong in the zoo.

AaBbCcDdEeFfGgH

QqRrSsTtUuVvWwX

GgHhIiJjKkLlMmNn

WwXxYyZzAaBbCcD

mNnOoPpQqRrSsTt

CcDdEeFfGgHhIiJj

SsTtUuVvWwXxYyZz